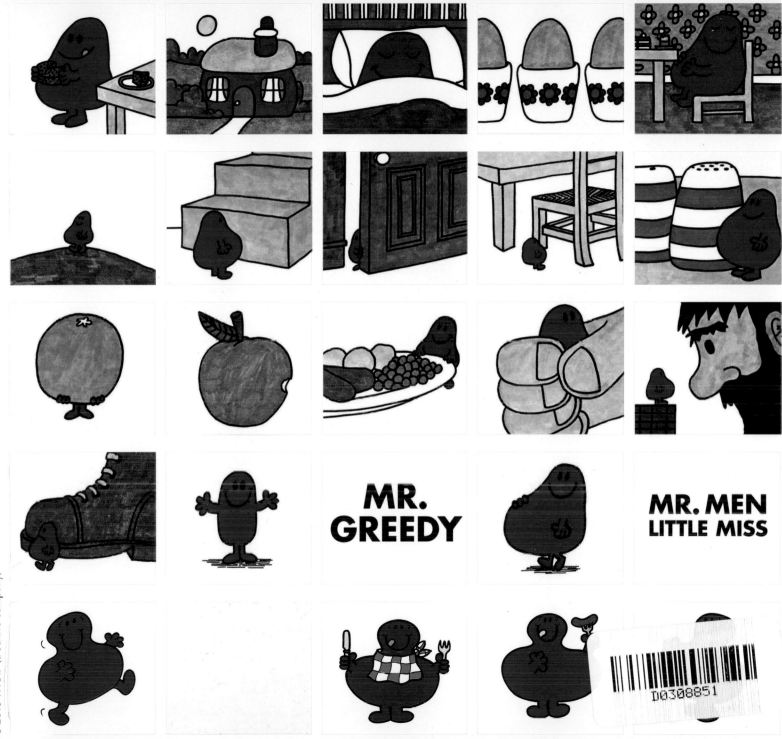

# MR. GREEDY

**MR. MEN**
**LITTLE MISS**

D0308851

# MY MR. GREEDY COLOURING BOOK

by Roger Hargreaves AND _____

Mr Greedy liked to eat!

In fact Mr Greedy loved to eat, and the more he ate, the fatter he became.

And the trouble was, the fatter he became, the more hungry he became.

And the more hungry he became, the more he ate.

And the more he ate, the fatter he became.

And so it went on.

Put your sticker here

Now copy and colour in!

Mr Greedy lived in a house that looked rather like himself.

It was a roly-poly sort of a house.

Put your sticker here

Now copy and colour in!

One morning, Mr Greedy awoke rather earlier than usual.

He'd been dreaming about food, as usual, and that had made him wake up feeling hungry, as usual.

So Mr Greedy got up, went downstairs and ate the most enormous breakfast.

Put your sticker here

Now copy and colour in!

This is what Mr Greedy had for his breakfast.

TOAST – 2 slices

CORNFLAKES – 1 packet

MILK – 1 bottle

SUGAR – 1 bowlful

TOAST – 3 slices

EGGS – 3 boiled

TOAST – 4 slices

BUTTER – 1 dish

MARMALADE – 1 pot

Put your sticker here

Now copy and colour in!

When he had finished his enormous breakfast,
Mr Greedy sat back in his chair, smiled a very
satisfied smile, and thought.

"That was a delicious breakfast," he thought to himself.
"Now I wonder what would be nice to have for lunch?"

He decided in order to work up an appetite for lunch he
would go for a long walk.

That morning, Mr Greedy walked and walked and walked.

Then he discovered a cave.

"That's funny," he thought, "I don't remember seeing that there before."

Mr Greedy, being a curious sort of a fellow,
decided to explore.

He entered the dark cave.

Inside he discovered some giant steps leading upwards.

Mr Greedy, being a curious sort of a fellow,
decided to climb them.

They were very steep and very difficult to climb,
but with much huffing and puffing Mr Greedy
climbed up and up.

Put your sticker here

Now copy and colour in!

At the top of the steps, Mr Greedy came to a door.

It was, without doubt, the biggest door that Mr Greedy had ever seen. And it wasn't quite shut.

Mr Greedy, being a curious sort of a fellow, decided to see what was on the other side of that door.

So Mr Greedy squeezed himself through the crack in the door, and there before him was an amazing sight.

The biggest room in the world!

Put your sticker here

Now copy and colour in!

The floor was as big as a field.

The table in the middle of the floor was as big as a house, and the chairs around it were as high as trees.

Mr Greedy felt very small.

Then he sniffed.

Coming from somewhere up on top of that gigantic table was the most delicious foody smell that Mr Greedy had ever smelled.

Put your sticker here

Now copy and colour in!

Mr Greedy sniffed again, and then decided that he must get up on to that table, so he began to climb up the leg of the enormous chair.

It was very difficult, and it took him a long time, but eventually Mr Greedy stood on the table.

Everything was larger than life.

The salt and pepper pots were both as big as pillar boxes.

Put your sticker here

Now copy and colour in!

There was a bowl of fruit on the table, and Mr Greedy
tried to lift one of the oranges.

Put your sticker here

Now copy and colour in!

And Mr Greedy, being Mr Greedy, took a bite out of one of the apples there.

Then he looked around.

Put your sticker here

Now copy and colour in!

Over on the other side of the table stood the source of that delicious smell.

A huge enormous gigantic colossal plate, and on the plate, huge enormous gigantic colossal sausages the size of pillows, and huge enormous gigantic colossal potatoes the size of beachballs, and huge enormous gigantic colossal peas the size of cabbages.

Mr Greedy hurried across the table towards the plate, and, being Mr Greedy, began to eat.

Put your sticker here

Now copy and colour in!

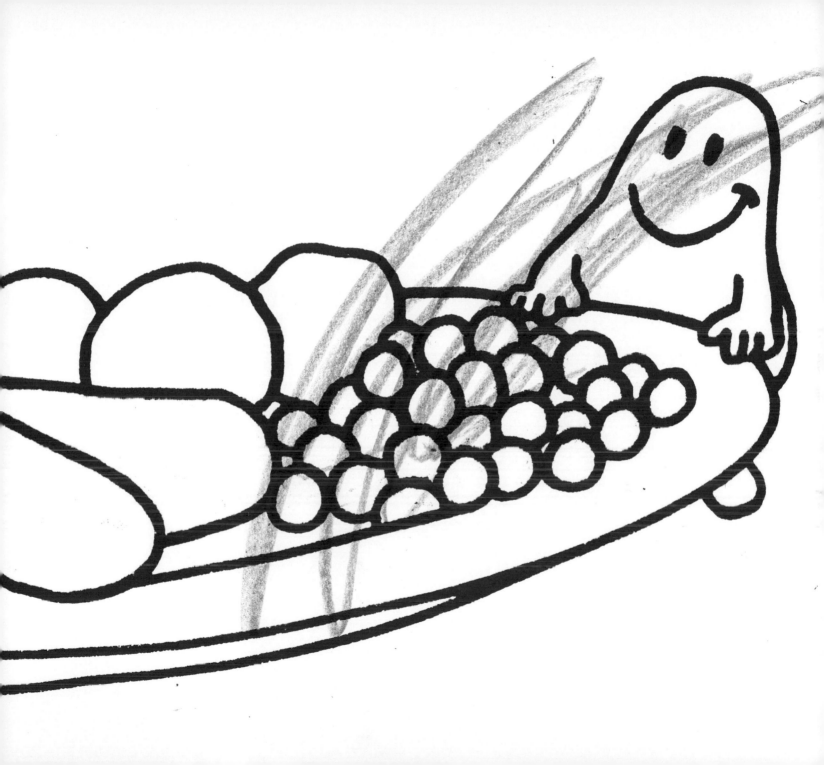

Suddenly, a shadow fell across the plate, and
Mr Greedy found himself being picked up by a giant
hand and looking into the eyes of a real live giant.

"AND WHO," thundered the giant, "ARE YOU?"

Mr Greedy was so frightened that he could only just
manage to squeak his name. "Mr Greedy,"
he squeaked.

The giant laughed a laugh as loud as thunder.
"GREEDY BY NAME AND GREEDY BY NATURE,"
he bellowed. "WELL I THINK
MR GREEDY THAT YOU NEED
TO BE TAUGHT A LESSON!"

Put your sticker here

Now copy and colour in!

And what a lesson it was.

The giant made Mr Greedy eat up everything on that huge enormous gigantic colossal plate.

When he had finished, Mr Greedy felt very ill indeed, as if he would burst at any minute.

"Now," said the giant in a much quieter voice, "do you promise never to be greedy again?"

"Oh yes," moaned Mr Greedy, "I promise!"

Put your sticker here

Now copy and colour in!

"Very well," said the giant, "then I'll let you go."

Mr Greedy climbed down from the table and went out through the door, feeling very fat and extremely miserable.

Put your sticker here

Now copy and colour in!

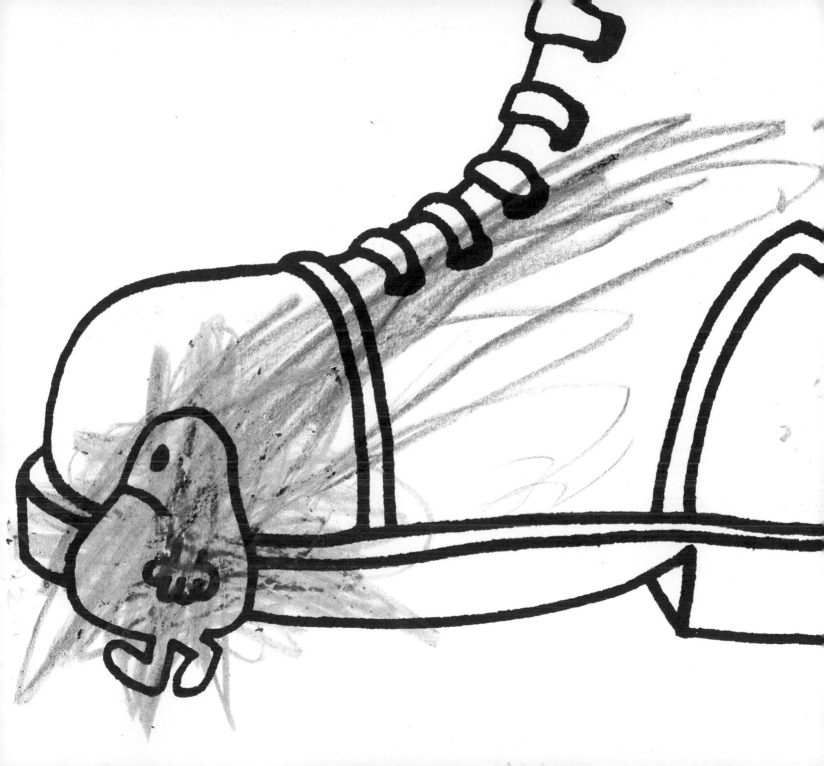

And do you know, from that day to this, Mr Greedy has kept his promise.

And do you know something else as well?

Mr Greedy doesn't look like he used to look any more.

He now looks like this, which I think suits him a lot better, don't you?

So, if you know anybody who's as greedy as Mr Greedy used to be, you know what to tell them, don't you?

Put your sticker here

Now copy and colour in!

Beware of giants!

I finished this book on _____ .

I am _____ years old.